Do Re Mi

Do Re Mi

by

GARSON
KANIN

Illustrated by

HIRSCHFELD

An Atlantic Monthly Press Book
Little, Brown and Company · *Boston* · *Toronto*

Published November 1955
Reprinted November 1955

DO RE MI originally appeared in the *Atlantic*.

ATLANTIC–LITTLE, BROWN BOOKS
ARE PUBLISHED BY
LITTLE, BROWN AND COMPANY
IN ASSOCIATION WITH
THE ATLANTIC MONTHLY PRESS

*Published simultaneously in Canada
by Little, Brown & Company (Canada) Limited*

PRINTED IN THE UNITED STATES OF AMERICA

Do Re Mi

I AM sitting here in the sneezer. Taking the fall for Fatso. Again. It is not so bad. They got a television now, only the food was better the last time. May be changed cooks. I hope I don't catch stomach trouble is all I hope.

Yesterday I had the Heart to Heart with the chaplin. Same joe as was, only this time older. Come to think, Im too. Older and dumber if not I would not got in here. Again. The chaplin is ok and no bull. He says, he is dis-app ointed to see me back in and I say like wise. He says, what happened. Well I should of told him how I am taking the fall for Fatso. Again. But than I figure whats the good. So he looks on my card and he says to me, you realize you are a three time loser. I say, you dont need to tell me chaplin I know it better then you also how one more time and I could get the Big Deal. He says, how do you think you are going to not. So I could of told him because this is the last time I take the fall for Fatso. but I did not. The hell of it is Fatso dont think I am taking the fall for Fatso. He knows it but he does not think it. He claims if not on acc ount me he would not of got in the "hot mustard." Go argue with him.

Any ways the chaplin says, I see you got six to ten. (Months) I say, yes sir. He points on the sign in the back to him. It says on it: DONT SERVE TIME — MAKE TIME SERVE YOU! I didnt get it the last time and I dont get it this time. But I dont want to hurt his feeling so I dont crack I just look sad and shake my head up and downwards. Next thing he says, have you thought over care full how this happened to you. I say, the breaks. He gives me, you ought to think over the hole thing right from the beginning so as to know how it happened and where you made your mi

3

stakes. I say, yes like as if it was a pinochle hand. He says, you got the idea.

Only my trouble is when ever I start in to thinking, I fall to sleep. I tell him this. He says, why dont you write it out. First I dont get it than he explains me. I say, ok. So now Im sitting here writing it out. He says it will be good for me, the chaplin. He gave me the loan of this book of the Webster's Dictionary and says, go to it. All I hope is I can finish by the time I have to get out because it takes time and I got to look up in the book of the Webster's Dictionary plenty of the words I am not too positiv how to spell them. And so far I am still on the store room crew and I am out of condition for the bendi ng it takes. So after supper I feel more like to lay in on my back or go to the movie when it is one, but he says (cha plin) this is better to do. He says, make time serve you. I didn't get it the last time and I dont get it the this time neither. But naturally I am bucking for the time off for good behavior and I am never sure whats good behavior but I think its if you do no matter what they tell you to. So:

I think the whole thing it started in that night in the Casa when they opened Beny Louis. And Peggy Ray. I am hanging around in there making a little legitimate book in the case any body. I am sitting up back against the wall with a nice broad, living. She was no killer on looks but she knows every thing. One of those kinds. Also talky. I am funny. I like them talky. And this one (Kay) she knew

4

it all and than some. Like if you would happen to say to her, who is that ballhead guy with the two pros. She would probably no doubt know. In cards and spades. I use to call her some time, The Information Booth.

So we are sitting there this night eating Hawaiian and pretty soon the show looks like it is getting set to start. Any ways the different waiters are bringing in different tables and they are putting them in the front of the ring side ones so the ones who had the ring side ones have not got the ring side ones no more. And there is a lot of beefi ng going on but no trouble. The band starts in coming back in and the next thing you know here comes more tables, they are getting smaller the tables and so is the space on the floor for the floorshow. It is a laugh how all these chumps and wine buyers they come out for a good time and they wind up sore. (as a boil) Pretty soon the lights they go out and the chorus comes on and they are right away bunking in to one other pretty bad on account the no room. So you could imagine how surprise they are and every body else when the waiters they start in to bring even a nother table and they stick it right down in the front of the middle and I couldnt hardly believe in it bec ause this table they stuck it right down in the front of L.M. (I dont care to write out his name because it makes me nervous to look at it, but he has been no doubt the hardest boy ever went and now he is one of the biggest pieces of this place so how come they put down in the front of him, in fact he just got put down him self in the

5

front of some person The Information Booth tells me
owns three four moving picture companys) So I cant wait
to see who is going to make this spot and in walks a joker
very skinny and tall and wearing glasses with a tuck on.
He has got an other guy with him looking practically the
same and two chicks who they look like they never been
in a joint before the way they are looking around.

They sit down the four and naturally champain. The
first guy has to be tall and he is sitting right in the front
of where L.M. cant see any thing but the back of the
guys crew cut. (L.M. is little in tallness) By this time
every body has gone back to watching the show because
these kids in the show they have not got much on them in
the way of dresses. But I personally have seen what they
have before, manys the time and any how I am interested
to see what is going to happen down on the ring side.
Nothing good I am ready to lay odds.

This has to be the time my broad with the answers she
picks to go in the powder. And when she goes its any bodys
guess when is she coming back on account of Helen who
works it is an old side kick of her and when they get in to
a smoosh it takes godknows some times. I dont complain
because I got the idea this is where mine picks up a lot of
her know. So I am sitting alone and watching what is
going to happen and pretty soon I see the Captain go on
over and L.M. says some thing to him. He dont look at
him mind you he just says and the Captain goes. A couple
minutes Toolio who is running the house comes over and
him and L.M. have a little buzz and the next thing Robbie

him self comes and he squats down and he blows some thing in L.Ms. ear I dont know what. Than L.M. makes a small yes with his head and Robbie squats away.

Well by this time the mc introduces Peggy Ray and she gets a great hand and she comes out and just before she starts in to sing she looks surprise and steps down and leans over and she gives this guy with the glasses a king size kiss right in his kisser. Than she goes back to sing and she does it fine but I am still watching this guy while he is wiping off the lip stick off of him laughing. After a while mine comes back and I ask her who is the guy. She looks down there and she says, mygod he is John Henry Wheeler. This means not a thing to me so I say, whose he. From Washington or what? She says, no only he is the biggest man in the song and music game. he has got pract ically most of the records and the juke boxes in his pocket. he can make a singer or a band or a song just on his own sayso. And she keeps on talking and telling me the whole story of his life which who cares. But I am looking at this guy and worrying how such a squirt gets to top such a take. It makes me nervous so I blow.

I go across the street to the little bin there and I drink my self a beer and I been in the place about a thousand and a half times and I never see the juke box there before. I say to Timmy, how long thats been here. Whats been, he says. The juke box. Always. I cant believe it. I go over and I study it over. I say to Timmy, this is better then the old slots, you know it. with this you never got to pay off no jack pot. also no law in your hairs. So I knock in a quarter

8

and damn if Peggy Ray dont start in singing the same song I left her singing across the street. It was Erie if you know what I mean. And than is when I made my big mistake. I thought of Fatso. That was my big mistake. I should not of.

2

WHY I thought of Fatso was, on account of the crack about the slots because that was the last hustle we got hooked up in together. Til that little La Guardia decides to get big so he goes hard nose and starts in to rough up every body in the slot business which was mostly Fatso. Who made up his mind to give the system a scrap only he come in second and I helped him to come in second. The gag he thought was: no sooner they picked up a Ma chine, the next day to stick in a nother one and I was the one was sticking. Than come the pinch (in Passaic) and the blow off. Fatso sends a counselor and the counselor tells me how to cop the plea and says if I am to mention Fatso it will be not too good. He tells me to play it cozy and Ill get off with a light and after, Fatso will see me. This is what I done. Only when I come out, Fatso is out. I mean out of business and out of town and his reputat ion is shaking and he cant operate nothing so he is back in Jersey City. I am in no kind of shape at all and the two skins they give me the day I am sprung do not give me the feeling of loaded by a longshot. I go to Jersey City. Fatso looks to be running a garage. I ask him what it is fronting and he says it is a garage and thats all. So I give him my sob and he gives me back a bigger one. Every thing in the wifes name and she slammed off with the college kid that use to be the accounting. So he says, good bye and goo dluck and dont bother me. I didnt feel sore in fact sorry for the guy he looks such a dead battery. He was never a rough man with a buck when he had it but I saw he was checked out so that was that. Things can certainly change. I would never of thought I would ever see a firstclass cha racter like he running a garage fronting nothing.

Getting back to that night in the bin across the Casa. I think of Fatso and how he organized the slots and holygod what he could do in this new touch and I get excited and lose my head and the next day I am on my way to Jersey City in Jersey.

First I miss the place because it is all changed around. Now it is still a garage but with like a bar and grill attached to. It is the morning and I go in. A guy is sweeping out and when I seen how it was Fatso I could of burst out. An other thing. Fatso has got so thin so when I say, how you Fatso, it does not sound even sensible. He looks at me and like squints and it takes him time to recognize me and the first thing he says, beat it. I say, whats a matter. He says, dont bother me. I say, I like to buy a sanawich and a cup of coffee off you. whats wrong with that. He goes in the back of the counter and does it and after a while we are talking friendly. While he is talking I feed the juke box and it plays. I say to him, whats your deal on that box. He says, search me. I go look on the side of it and sure enough there is a little sign tacked on to it says, WHEELER

12

CORPORATION. I say, whats youre cut. Nothing no cut, he says. they put it in and change the records and it costs me nothing for music in the joint which you got to nowad ays. I walk back to him and I say, how about if I ask you to put in a box, the same as that may be better and every countup I throw you ten per cent? Fatso puts down his broom. I can see he is beginning to dig me. The one thing he was always sharp. You in that business, he asks me? No, I say to him, WE are. He dont answer a thing he just goes around the back of the bar and he opens up a bottle of rye and he pours out two shots and he pushes me one and he knocks back his and he says to me, talk.

So I get going and I tell him how this is the hottest thing going and about the Wheeler guy and how all it needs is organization and who is the best? Him. All the time I am giving it he is looking at the music coming out of the box. Finely he says, the only thing I made up my mind I took the oath never again not, only strictly legitim ate from now on. Im getting too old for the rackets. I look him in the eyes and I tell him, you aint old Fatso. you only act old. you are in youre prime. He says, just the same. I say, what is un legitimate about this thing. name me one. He says, keep going. So I do my pitch, the one I practiced up on the train going out. I say, the way it looks to me here is some thing big which is practically like the slots only bigger and up and up. I figure you and some of the other slot characters are with the experience and the talent to take over or if not get your selfs a piece.

At this Fatso pours him self an other shot and puts it

away. Than he looks at me, not mad but almost and he says to me, soft, (I got a very nasty feel in my back of my spine when I hear that soft way of his again) He says, when you say other slot characters, what have you got in youre mind. I say, take it easy a minute. so far this is all talk. you are the first I have mentioned to. I am no org anizer. thats you. I am just the connecter. you are the boss, Boss. He says, keep going. I say, I see where this needs three points. one is the organization. two is dough. three is a little power, like "salesmanship." He says, so far you are one thousand per cent right all the way. who is two and three. I say, up to you. He says, dont stall me. who you got in youre mind. I say, well like, this is just gassing you under stand but like for instance I would say for the dough part may be like well say for instance — like say — Skin.

Soon as I said out this name, Fatso looks at me (red) but I do not flinch. He says, take off. I say, what goods that. by gones are by gones. Thats right, he says, and crumbs are crumbs. I say, the only difference this is a crumb with some chips. Fatso says, I ought to know some of them are my chips. if no body else can you ought to be able remember the cross he threw us that crumb. after we made up to stick in every time they pulled out, does he? no. he keeps selling us his Machines so he winds up with a roll and we wind up with a rap. I wind up, I says, who done the bit after all? Thats right, so how come you got the crust bringing his name up. (About now I can see my whole hot flash in the ash can) I say, so what if you would of wound up with more so would you have it now. no. you know who would, and her college friend. Im talking right out plain Fatso. He talks soft again (the way I dont like it so much) and he says, you sure in the hell are boy. if I was you I would watch it. I say, just the same if we could get him to be willing why not. Ill think it over, he says. who is number three. Legs, I say. A very good number three, Fatso says, only you forgot one detail. he is dead. Since when, I say. Since he died, Fatso gives me. You got him mixed, I say, he aint dead, he is running a chicken farm in Upstate New York. that was his brother took it that time. Fatso says, I remembered they both took it. No, I say, you are remembering wrong. Well, if he is not cooled, Fatso says, he is a good man for the power. I say, you mean the "salesmanship." Thats what I said, Fatso says. So we keep up talking it over and over and we finish the bottle of rye. We are figuring every thing every whic hway and it looks good. I am stiff as a board around now, but not him. He was always like that. It is like milk to him. So we make up that the next day we go to Upstate New York and try it with Legs.

3

On the train I show Fatso a few books I bought. They are Variety, billboard, and Downbeat. These books tell all about the business we are practically in. It looks to be full of nothing but money. We are looking over the big sellers and singers. Fatso says, if these are all so wellknown these songs how come I never heard a one. I say, they are all on your Machine. He says, I never heard them. Because you dont listen, I say. from now on we got to listen beca use this is going to be our business. I know songs, when I was a kid I took violin. didnt you? He says, no. my kid sist ers took piano, not me. Didnt you take any thing, I ask him? He says, sure I took any thing wasnt tied down. Than he laughs. Very hard. So I too. (from the olden days I remember that when ever Fatso laughed every body else had to also if not he didnt like it) Now he looks out of the window for a long time, and he says, I can see we are going to have to have a number four. What for, I say. A music expert, he says. They are a dime a dozen, I tell him. Never mind dozen, he says (mean) one is all we need. He was starting in to sound like the old time Fatso.

From the Gloversville Station we call up. Legs is surpr

ised. We go out in a old car that is suppose to be a taxi. The farmer charges us one-eighty. I pay and I am beginning to see this better work out because I am getting to have a nice little investment tied up here. Legs is sure glad to see us and he shows us around his chicken farm which I didnt care if he did or not. His mrs comes in. I remember her from the way back. When she use to do a turn in the joints. Singing and dancing. She always had plenty of stuff but it was not in her singing and dancing. Other places. She looks different now. A little I would say on the hefty side and a touch of gray in the head and the dress she is wearing is like as if she would of made it for her self. I say, hello Thelma. She says you dont know me mister. I dont? No, no more. So I crack, small world. She says, thats right and getting smaller all the time. Than she turns in to Legs and she says, what is going on around here. He says, you got me there dearest. the boys said they want to see me. She says, didnt you tell them you didnt want to see them. Me and Fatso are looking each other bugeyed. She talking so up to him. In the olden days he was known to throw manys the punch at male and female both. Now he sits there egg on his face. He says, please Thelma. She says, outside. And that is where we wind up if you believe in it or not. In a chicken house and that is where we talk over this million dollar trick. He goes for it like I never seen a guy. Especially he likes how it is not un legitimate. Only he says he has got to talk it with Thelma and if she can see the light of day ok. But he is worried and says, the only thing how Im going to get her to go for the idea of this

20

is a level with you two folks in on it. But he says give him a couple three days and he will get square.

So we get ready to goof off. He makes us each take a dozen of eggs. Fresh. Then he walks us to wheres the bus. When it is starting in coming we every one shake hands. Fatso says, I was glad to see you Legs especially on account of how I understood you are dead. Legs says, nothing to it. We get on the bus where I leave my eggs on purpose on the seat and it begins to look we are off to the races.

By the end the week the three of us are sitting talking to Skin. Him we go see by the track and he takes us on between bets. He is got older too, the same like the rest of every body. Also he looks to be a little green around the gills and is developed a nervous "tick" I think they call it. Every body remembers Skin they remember how he was all the time flipping him self a half of a dollar. Up and down up and down. And he is still doing it, the same thing. The only thing, he keeps missing it all the time and I am grovelling around on the ground half the time finding it for him. Some he loses. No body makes a mention of his aim and he keeps on flipping. Trying to I mean to say. He listens good though and when he has got the picture, he says, ok guys deal me in. So every body shakes every bodys hands and from here out, action.

The first thing was an office. This is on fourty nineth street for two hundred and fourty a month with the loft for Machines. The name got picked was The Music Ent erprise Associates, Inc. To me this is a stupid name but the idea came from Skin and at that time no body was in a position to argue (on account of him being the staker) so no body argued. Skin put out for a bash of Machines (secondhanded). Also there was a ton and a half ton truck for the hauling and other stuff what ever we needed for the lay out.

The way it started out it was so cinchy that it was no enjoyment hardly. Just for the luck of it, the four of us took on the first press. Right across the street from where we took the office is a good busy bar. We go in together the four. We all stand around a minute. A guy is mopping. Legs talks. Lets have the boss, son. (The guy must of been seventy odd, so he calls him son. That is Legs for you) The mop guy is so scared he practically runs practically. Two minutes a large-sized type of man comes in. Legs waits for him to get close. The four of us are standing looking. The boss says, what can I do for you fellows. Legs gets right on the top of him almost and he says very low, who you getting youre music from, Mack? The boss looks over us and he says, why from you fellows. Very good answer, Legs says. very healthy. we stick our box in here after lunchtime. get this one out. Thats right, says the boss. lets have a drink. So we every body have a drink. Now Fatso explains him the deal with the ten per cent cut and the guy likes it. Then he says, the saloon keeper, I dont want to tell you men how to run youre business the only thing I hope you dont load up the box with classical and opera. they are not for the type of crowds I get in here. I know some places, like spaghetti joints, they do a good trade with Caruso stuff but in here it just lays there. here they

22

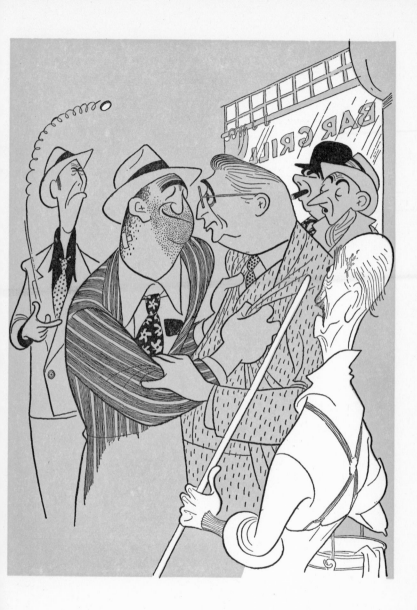

like loud dame singers and all the number one tunes. (We are all listening like crazy because it is no mistake this guy knows more about what we are suppose to know about then we know our self) Skin says, dont worry about it. we will give you the best. We go.

The first day we spotted every Machine (Twenty) and by the end of it every body is feeling oatsy. It looked like the ship not only come in but docked and unloaded. My only beef was how no body seemed to remember who it was had the idea. I. Only no respect or mention. I guess once a stooje always.

Every thing gets to be on the move and we are learning fast and the first thing we find out is twenty Machines is nothing. So the next, Fatso starts in to whip and right away we spotted over two hundred. (by now firsthanded) This is more like it and the collections start in to begin amount to some thing. What is wrong. Nothing. We are doughed up good, the all of us. Personally I am putting away steak (welldone) every night in Gallaghers. One thing I did not mention so far, in fact I forgot it on purp ose because when it happened I did not want to rem ember it. But I do and will put it down because I am suppose to every thing. It was a few weeks after we are on the way. Legs is in the charge of spotting the Mac hines and every so often I go with him for backing up. In a lot of the places they seem to know who is Legs and if not they seem to get the idea he is not play full. It is going like a "fixed" fight. No trouble. There is a little gosiping but Fatso says forget it. Even one time there

24

is a thing in Danton Walkers about guess who is now runn
ing the biggest juke box business in town you would be
surprised. Legs is for having a chat with him so as to adv
ice him. About how it would be better to clam. Fatso
says, lay off, so far he is free advertising if he keeps on
saying we are the biggest may be we will get to be. Legs
feels different but every thing is going so good no body
wants to tangle amongst each other.

But about what I forgot: one morning after lunch time
Legs and me step down to the Village. This is a new terr
itory we have not even touched. There is a place there
with the name of Sullivans. We go in to the inside of it.
There is no body there only a small Redhead man. Legs
says, I like to see the boss, son. Redhead says, I am him,
son. (Legs did not go for this man right off) Legs says,
we are putting a music box in here today or else tomorrow
instead of the one you got there. Redhead says, what
makes you think so. Legs says, I am telling you. Redhead
smiles and he says polite, I am satisfied the way I am.
So I can see may be trouble so I say, we can make you
a better deal. we give ten per cent of the countup. At this
Legs hots up and he says to me, since when your handling
this. So I back up. He walks over to the man and he says,
what about it. The man says, ten per cent is a nice nu
mber only I dont want youre Machine in here. Legs says,
why. Redhead says, because I don't like the way you do
business coming in here like some old time hoodlum and
telling me what you are going to do in my place and not
asking. That is tough, Legs says. Now Redhead says, goo

dbye, and he turns away. Legs steps after him and gives him a spin around. I was nervous because this was the first time muscle. Redhead gets white. (in his face) Legs says, I don't want to have to put you through the grinder mister. The man says, well that makes two of us so we dont have to bother. Legs says, ok than how about it. Redhead says, just a second. With this he moves two three bar stools away and a table with some dishes on it and a coat rack. I cant figure out what is he doing. Legs neither. Now he steps back to Legs and he takes off his glasses (he was wearing glasses) and he says, now you want to step out or can you use some help. Legs reaches inside of his vest and just when he done this Redhead throws a kind of stupid looking round house punch and it catches Legs on the side of his head, and it knocks him right out from under his hat. I know this is hard to believe, but I seen it. Legs winds up looking surprise, sitting in a booth holding on to his ear and his hat comes down right on the spot where he was stan ding before. And sick to his stomach. Then Redhead takes a step to me (of all people) He says, how about you. I said, no thanks. I realize this was a child-ish thing to say but I am trying to put down the truth the whole truth and nothing but the truth like you are supposed. Next stop: to the doctor because Legs claimed his ear was hur ting him some thing terrible so we went. He told the doctor he had ran in to some person by mistake, which was not exactly a "lie" if you look at it in the right way.

That night was a meeting and Legs told that he did

not think the Village was any good because all the ope
rations down there are too small and also he heard the
kind of persons who ran it are un reliable. He says, ask
Hubie he will tell you. (Hubie is my name. Hubert) Every
body looks at me and I say, it is no good down there.
Than me and Legs look to gether and I know who ever
I am ever going to have trouble with he is not one of them.

Village or no Village every thing is going hotstuff
when all a sudden we run into the first ditch. We start
in to getting calls from our different customers, they want
the Joe Stratton I BELONG TO YOU which is very big just
than. I call up where we get our platters and I start in
to chew the guy out for not putting it in and he gives
me, it aint available. I say, dont give me that it is on pra
ctically every box in town. He says, Wheeler boxes only.
it is his record. I tell this to Fatso and the boys and the
next thing they send for Wolfie (our record man) to talk
to. Wolfie starts in to tell them the facts of life and they
turn out to be the kind of facts that are not too good.
Once and a while they look at me as if to say you stink.
What can I do. Wolfie says a record like the one we
are asking is a Wheeler job because Wheeler has got the
control of Joe Stratton and he makes her records on spec
ial deals so that he has got exclusive on the box rights.
Wolfie says, you boys are beginning to have a big bash
here and may be you should have your own artists. Wolfie
blows. I speak, well we are living and learning. Fatso
says, well learning any how. He was in a not good mood.

4

This is how we got in to looking for our own talents.
The way Fatso caught on right away he is some "genius."
We all started in to go from one place till the other,
looking. I got a hold of Kay (The Information Booth)
and she took me to a place to hear some blue singer,
who she said is great. I could not tell if or not. Fatso was
going around the different agents. Legs asked his wife
and his wife said how about my old partner Russ? This
did not go good with Legs and the day this Russ come
in to sing for us Legs was hoping he would turn out a
foul ball and he got his wish. I brought up my blue singer
and no body went for. Skin come up with a great idea,
he says, lets get Bing Crosby. So we had to straighten him
out. We all come up empty except Fatso, at least he
found this novelty gazoo band, they played on all different
sizes of gazoos.

We sign them under contract and they make a two
sided record and we put it on the Machines and it does
only fair. No loss but just about paid off. These gazoo
guys were ambitious and took us a couple months to get
rid of, they kept coming up all the time with new ideas

and arrangements and driving us crazy. They would come in morning noon or the night and some time if Fatso would say how we were busy and did not have the time, they would start in playing out side any way. In fact the next few months we never knew when they were going to turn up which they did all the time.

Than we hear The Jazz Brothers (they are a big act) are changing over and there is a chance to get them. So we go to The William-Morris-office to hear their new stuff. It is ok. But when we start to hear the kind of a deal they have got in their mind, or that is the kind of a deal their agent has got in their mind — we can see it is not for us, or that is, not for Skin who is still our chip man and he is beginning to worry because with all the trouble so far the best we can seem to be able is break even. And like Skin says, this good I could do playing favorites in Jamaica. So we go from The William-Morr is-office and naturally just as we are coming out who is coming in but this big guy John Henry Wheeler. My guys dont know it and I dont tell them.

Than came the BIG THING. We get in the elevator the four of us and no body is feeling any good. The elev ator girl is a cute little head with long hair hanging down til here. We get in the elevator and she steps out. We wait. Fatso says, lets go honey. She says to him, Im sorry sir I have to get my signal. Fatso, mad. She is snapping her fingers like I never heard. Sounding like a tap dancing. Pretty soon she gets in and starts the car. She keeps on snapping her fingers and the next thing you know she is singing and whistling together at the same time it sounds like. The god damnest thing I ever heard. Next thing you know we are all listening to her and we close in. Every body claims he was the one got the idea but I was there and to tell the truth the truth is that every body got the idea the same time. We must of stayed in that elevator for twenty minutes. A fellow from The William-Morris-offi ce told me after how he was downstairs waiting and he was watching that thing tells where is the elevator and he couldn't figure out if he was going crazy or what bec ause the way it was going back and forth and up and down and never got to the top and never the bottom. What was happening was Fatso wouldnt let her land, this lon ghair girl, and he kept making her sing some more and ask her where does she come from and all that.

It turns out she is a southern girl (from the South) Nin eteen years of age from Tennessee. What she is doing in New York is she is going to beauty school at night and putting her self through it with this running the elevator job. Well by the time she run it up and down a few dozen times every thing was changed around and when she finely did get it to the bottom Fatso took her by the one arm and Legs by an other arm and took her right the hell out. She was squawking a little and hollering she had to turn in her uniform and she couldnt leave the elevator, but no body listened. There were some people in the lobby of it there wondered what the hell, but I laughed it up and Skin too so every body thought some joke. Well we take her right to the office and Fatso sends for the counselor and he tells

the girl she is going to be the biggest thing lately if she plays her cards right and she says the only thing I dont know if I can do it in the front of any body and Legs says whats that? This is going to be all on records so from than on it was ok.

Naturally I dont have to put it down here that this is Nan Needles because any body with ears on in the USA has heard her by now. At that time we didnt know our self about her playing the zither. All we knew was the singing and the whistling and the snapping the fingers.

A week after, we cut the first record. CRAZY AS A CRICKET. The whole thing was getting to be breezyr and breezyr bec ause it turned out so we hardly ever had to worry what this kid should sing or buying numbers or like that because she was full of numbers she said she learned them from back home (South) in school or on the hay ride. So she makes CRAZY AS A CRICKET and TENNESSEE HAYRIDE on the other side and this turns out a mistake on account of them two goes one and two. So than we split them up and backed up each one with some nothing she happen to remember so than the two nothings goes even bigger. No body could make it out. Her and her zither is the hottest thing going. Like Fatso says one night, boys it looks like we have caught the lightning in a bottle.

They start in going like hardcakes, the records, and we have got them and her and every thing is the most ac ey-douchey it has been for some time. Offers. That is what we started in to get. This one wants her. And that one. But Fatso is not going for nothing. Wolfie tells us a good thing would be she should go do it some place where the

people can see her in the person. So we think. It is anypl ace we want. In the Paramount or the Casa or the Wald orf. Big argument. Every body has got some own idea. But she her self is for the Waldorf. Why? Because how she tried to get a job there on the elevators and they give her the turn down. So that is why she holds out for the Waldorf.

While we are deciding to make up our mind a funny thing happens. Very. We are all in the Mecca for a session and pretty soon we got the take and getting ready to leave, Legs says, wait a second. Sit down every body. Than in comes a small five piece combo and a girl. Legs says, I want every body listen to this certain special song and give theyre opinion. The combo starts in and the girl puts glasses and starts in to sing from the lead sheet. And she gets about as far as:

> *I love you because you are you*
> *I love you so what can I do*
> *Your eyes and all your other things*
> *To my heart the sunlight brings*
> *I love you because you are you*

About that far and Legs is looking around I dont know why is he "sweating" like a stung pig but he can see from the different looks on the different faces that it is going over like acres of nothing. He jumps up and he says no no no no. Every thing stops. He says to the singing woman, that is all wrong. She says, you are so right. She hands him back the lead sheet and she goes on out. Legs throws off his coat and opens up his collar and he is like got hyste

36

ricals, he hollers to the combo, slower and a heavy beat this is a waltz for Christ sake. So they play a intro and no body could be more surprise then us when he starts in (Legs) and he sings. He sounds like tenor or what ever it is Mort on Downey and Phil Regan do. But whorse. May be the sound is more along the line of Talulia (not in the book of the Webster's Dictionary here) Banghead. Any way. He is singing his heart out and selling the number and about half of the way through he is crying and you can practically hear it in his pipes. And the song goes like this: at least the words go like:

> *I love you because you are you*
> *I love you so what can I do*
> *Your eyes and all your other things*
> *To my heart the sunlight brings*
> *I love you because you are you*
> *And Im one whos known quite a few*
> *When we first met you gave your hand*
> *Never knew a touch so grand*
> *Lifes been a scheme where*
> *Ive missed you*
> *Manys the dream where*
> *Ive kissed you*
> *Dont change into somebody new*
> *I love you because you are you*

This is the words of the song Legs sung. Every body is quiet. Than we stand up. Legs is puffing. He says, well how do you like the song. Fatso says, I can still smell it.

38

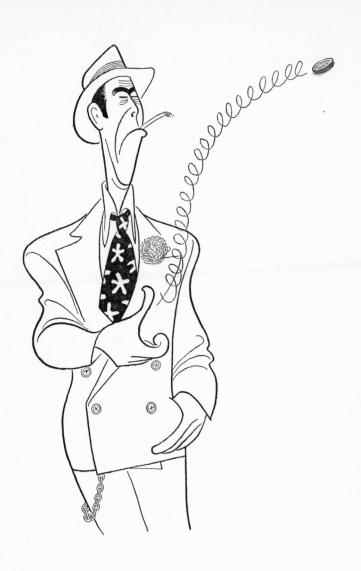

Well that did it. No matter how I am trying here to stick to the truth the whole truth and nothing but the truth, it is no use. I could not tell what happened from than on for quite a while. I know it started with Legs walks over and swings on Fatso and thangod he missed because it could of took off a mans head. Skin jumps in to stop the next try and sure thing he has to catch it him self. He throws one back on Legs but Legs is going for Fatso again and so how did I get hit my self. The thing made it funny was every body out of condition and missing and hitting the wrong guy and picking up the different music instrum ents happening to be laying around there. It went on for quite a while, finely it stopped and we all went down stairs to the bar to cool off.

In the booth there we looked lousy. There wasnt a one didn't have a bandade or a cut or torn clothes. After the first beer Fatso says quiet to Legs, what hit you man? Legs says, where do you come off passing a remark like that about that song. Fatso: my opinion. why fly off. holygod it is like as if you wrote the song your self. Legs just stays miserable. Skin looks at him and says: holygod did you. Legs says, no. but Thelma did. (his wife) We all look each other and now Fatso gets hot and he says, well why the hell didnt you say so you cheese head. Legs says, bec ause. So than we every body had an other beer. And sha king hands all around. Still and all Fatso says, business is business and I cant help if your wife did or didnt. it is no good and cant use it. Legs says, since when you turned in to such an expert. Fatso says, since youre wife turned

40

in to such a song writer. Legs says, I may sell out. Fatso: Im ready to buy any time. Legs: name a number. Fatso: twenty five. Legs: forget it. I got an offer already more than twice it. Fatso: so what are you waiting for. So on the side walk we split up and Skin says, come on Nan I will take you home. (by this time we got her a suit in the Waldorf so to be convenient)

5

THE next morning on the crack of dawn (around noon time) who should get me on the phone if not Nan and she has got to see me, she says. I pile out and go over. She says, I have to tell you about last night. I say, go ahead. She says Skin brought me home and he did not act like a gentle man. what do you know about that? I say to her, Nan that is the most worst thing I have ever heard in my life what you have just told me. (I am putting it on a little because the truth is I had it in my mind to not act like a gentle man with her my self in the case I ever got an opening and so I am burned now Skin beat me to the punch a little) She says, I dont know what to do because I love him as a brother or uncle and I owe him a hole lot. I look at her (with some sex in it) and I say, you dont owe him no more then you owe me. She says, I know it. I am crazy about all you boys but not that way. and I dont want any thing to spoil every thing. You are right there, I say, so what is it you want me to do? She says, would you mention to Skin, I dont know how to with out hurting his feeling. I say, Nan I will do any thing for you I can but if I should mention to Skin the chances are he would hurt MY feeling and may be some thing else too. Skin is not the type of person it is easy to tell any thing because he has got too much money. She says, he even said about he would like to get married. to me. (this surprised me I dont mind telling) She says, but I guess that is just a line. do you think I ought to may be mention this to Mr. Brunio? (she means Fatso) I say, no — you saw the kind of free for all can develop with this bunch even over a small thing so if it was over a large thing like you it could be even worse. She says, I am worried and I dont know what to do. I say, do nothing and dont worry. the only thing you got to worry is knocking them dead in the Wald orf. She says, ok. I say, and dont worry about Skin he is just a fresh character and he ought to be a shamed of him self and if he ever tries again the thing is to give him the key to the street. and dont let him bring you home no more. in fact, I will see to it personally that I am the one brings you home from now on. She says, oh that is great. thank you. With this I walk over and I take and plant one of my own on her and when I come up she is looking at me (funny) as if she doesnt know am I kidding or what — and I do not give her any help right now but I just turn away and keep going. In fact I walked about fifty (50) blocks before I stop.

The next few days nothing happened about nothing except the Waldorf business. In the papers, ads. On the Waldorf, signs. And all over town, posters. Nan is getting nervous, a little.

Now every body starts in to tell her what to do and

show her and coach her. Legs is showing how he thinks, which is old hat the way his wife use to in the silver Sli pper. And he thinks she ought to be low cut dresses in the front. At this Fatso starts in to raise holyhell. He says she ought to do it more cute, like a small kid. This is no May West, he says, this is more of a Shirley Temple. Skin does not like this idea, naturally he wouldnt. Legs says, or like that babytalk girl use to. (In case you remember. Boob boob a doob) I get the idea she should put on her elevator operator suit. Every body "razzberries" this idea. (I still think it would of been good personally) Than Fatso comes up with the saddest yet. That she should not put make up on her head. And a gingham dress. And sing barefooty! I said she will catch a cold and than what. But Fatso was turning in to like a real I-guy. The next thing where are we. Waldorf. And the kid is going to be on. The joint is packed. I am a shame to say it but I was wea ring one of those with the tails. Fatso made every body. Including him self. We looked some thing terrible. Me with a coat hanging down in the back. (every time I moved I thought some body is following me!)

Just before she is going to go on we are all in the back with her on account she is still nervous to do it in the front of people. But we tell her how the lights will be out and so make out no body is looking. There are plenty of flowers in there. The most looks like a whole basket of orchids and Skin looks at the card on it and he says, whats this. And Nan says, it says From John Henry Wheeler I dont even know him. Fatso says, well see that you dont.

46

We each give her one kiss (cheek) for (luck) and we go. The lights are starting in to go down and pretty soon we are going after two waiters who are carrying a table down to put it in the front of the ring side. There is us four and Legsis mrs (Thelma) and I have brought my broad (The Information Booth). Where do they put the table but sure enough right in the front of the one where who is sitting but John Henry Wheeler and a nother like him and two dames full of icebergs on them. He is just wearing a plain regular tuck. So we looked at him as if to say. But to tell the truth even though there was plenty there got up like us (with the tails) I could not of felt wackier if I would of been wearing a bathing suit. The lights are out and on the speaker is playing soft a zither and right away there is a big hand. A voice introduces her, very fancy. A spot light. Out comes Nan and with one arm carrying her zither and in a nother arm dragging a plain like a kitchen chair. She sits down and the place goes quiet. Except one table is still yakking. Fatso goes over. So they stop. No trouble. (But could of been the way he went) She starts in to go and you could of heard a pen drop. People get to be crying and some holding hands and a funny thing when she finished the first song I figured was going to be a big hand but no. Every body just sat. She goes again and I dont know what it was but by the time she got finished we were all crying our self. Then she got some reception.

After the show we are all feeling firstclass and persons are coming over to our table and saying she is great. Later on I am doing some Rhumba with Thelma and I look over and Nan has come out from behind. She looks different. All gussied up with paint on and a regular dress and she is some hit. Pretty soon I see Wheeler get up from his table and he moves over to where ours is. I Rhumba over there fast, in case. He is introducing him self all over the place to Fatso and every body and they all sit there looking at him hard, but he dont notice it and than he tells Nan how she is the greatest thing and the next he asks her for a dance and Skin says, no. But either Nan didnt hear him or she makes out like she didnt and Wheeler neither and the next they are up there dancing. I figure it is time to go back so Thelma and me stop and we sit down. Fatso says, Legs it looks to me you got a little job on. Legs says, how far you think we can go. Fatso says, we better talk this guy and if not who knows you may have to rough him up a little. Legs looks to me and I to him and we are both thin king no doubt of the Red Head in the Village. Legs says, well lets see what happens. So we all watch on the floor and that John Henry Wheeler looks to be doing fine and she too.

6

THE next day we are having a meeting except Legs he is not there. Fatso says how he is been up half the night worrying the Wheeler situation. He says, that is all we need is to lose that kid, the chances of finding a nother one like her is about the longest shot going. Skin says, may be if I took her out and "romanced" her a little. I dont mind doing it for the good of the business. (he says all this with his straight face!) Fatso says, dont talk so stupid she would probably laugh in your puss. Well, we are arguing this back and forth and the guy from Mecca comes in with the new sides we done with Nan. Than he says, there is no label on the backup yet because we cant find the artist credit. Fatso says, what backup. The guy says, this one. We put it on the Machine and out comes I LOVE YOU BECAUSE YOU ARE YOU for godsake. With Legs singing. Fatso says, thats nothing. a bobble. The guy says, ok but what name for the label. Fatso says, no name. put some dummy name thats all. The guy does. And we all have a good laugh. Skin says, is this ok to do. Fatso says, dont worry. who will know the differents. I say, Legs will. Fatso says, may be not it sure dont sound like him. Skin says, it dont sound like any body. And that is the truth.

This is around when Nan shows up the way Fatso told her he wanted she should. Our idea was to nip her bud.

(with Wheeler) Fatso wanted to not to do it but that is what it was decided. Some body sure in the hell had to bec ause all we needed was this Wheeler "bastard" moving in. So Fatso said ok he will handle the whole thing, only priv ate, if not, than not. So when Nan shows, Fatso gives us the office to goof off and that is what we do. Skin asks me for coffee, but I tell him I cant handle it I got to work in the back. (Lie) What I wanted, I wanted to get the load of Fatso giving it to her. So I go around in the back there and than I move in the room the next one to him (and her). And I lean by the door and catch the ear full. The walls there being around the size of a slice of ham in a on e-arm, I heard good. This is what I heard: I wouldnt say word for word under oath but the idea was like this:

HIM (FATSO): See I feel a father to you and the boys the same.

HER (NAN): Well I certainly am a lucky girl to have four fathers.

HIM: Not only that but we are all partners and the best thing is not forget we are partners.

HER: I never forget it. morning noon and night.

HIM: See the reason this is hard to talk is I dont know how much you know about things.

HER: What things.

HIM: Take like men. Im talking about the kind of men we have in the city of New York and what they are after.

HER: We have them in Tennessee too.

HIM: Not like here honey. believe me.

52

HER: Oh yes.

HIM: Any how you know we dont want to but in your private life.

HER: Thank you.

HIM: Only we dont think it is a good thing you moving around with this Wheeler punk.

HER: He is a nice boy.

HIM: We dont want you moving around with him.

HER: Why not.

HIM: Because he is not on our side and that is no bull. he is giving you a little song and dance on account you are a hot property and that is all. it is a funny thing. you will find out when you grow up older. if some body tells some other body some thing it doesnt have to be the truth.

HER: I think you are getting too excited too soon because so far all the fellow did is ask me to have a dance with him and today sent flowers.

HIM: Send them back!

HER: No thank you.

HIM: If you are going to turn out to be a nerve tester I am not going to enjoy it.

HER: What girl doesnt like a little attention.

HIM: It depends from who. cant you see that. honey.

HER: I dont get much of a chance to. if I am not rehear sing I am recording or taking my picture or godknows.

HIM: I know how you feel. honey. you know I am lone some my self. In fact I am all alone. may be some time we could have a date together. I think you are a fine girl.

HER: I think you are a fine man but I dont want to have a

date with you. or Skin neither. and so far as Hubie is concerned.

This is about the much as I heard. When she got to the mention of my name (Hubie) I checked out. I couldnt stand it to hear what she was going to say. Also I figured there is a chance she is going to spill about the pass. (Skins, also me) But I believe she must not of because Fatso never mentioned.

7

THAT night we are all hanging around the Waldorf again. (Only not with the monkey suits this time) Nan is on and she knocks them side ways again. Than we sit around and Fatso tells how he had this talk with her and it looks not too good. Legs says, may be we ought to give her a little shake. Fatso says, yes no doubt you could rough HER up all right if you could make the weight. Legs says, what in the hell kind of crack is that? Fatso says, forget it. Legs says, next time YOU forget it before you say it that will be better. Skin says, ok how about we stop boyscouting around here. Whats to do.

With this we notice Nan comes out and she goes to a table up against the wall and who is sitting there but Wheeler and he stands up when she comes there and than they both sit down next to one other the two of them and start in to holding hands. All we can do is look. Skin is flipping his coin and naturally he drops it and he looks to me and I holler out, pick it up youre self for once. And I go. I dont know whats got in to me. I go around the corner and I am stiffer then a board in nothing flat.

We had a nother meeting. Fatsos place. And the only thing was, have to have a talk with the Wheeler guy him self. It is going to be no joke. So we go. Every body in the car and no talking. It was like the olden days on a job.

We get to the place and it was some place. Three four stories of a building. The floors are shiny and nothing but different moderistic furniture and all the broads around are pretty moderistic them self. What a place. We give our name. They say, oh yes. come right in. And one of the little young broads takes us down one hall and up an other one and the place is loaded with all kinds of music business and piano playing and rehearsing and recording and arran ging. I never seen such a place. Than we come to the big office. It didnt even look like no office. More like some living room. And this guy Wheeler shakes hands all around and offers have a drink. I am set to grab, Fatso says, no. Next he brings out a big box of cigars. (Corona Corona) I see Legs is ready to take. Fatso says, no. After a while, Wheeler starts off, what can I do for you Fellows. Fatso says, I give it to you short and sweet. lay off. Wheeler laughs or else smiles, he says, how do you mean. Fatso stands up and says, dont give me them baby blues mister. every body here knows the score. Im telling you keep off the grass. Wheeler says, I didnt know I was on any grass. Fatso says, how would you like it we started in romancing YOURE propertys. you want to play rough you came to the right place. Wheeler says, you have me wrong. if you are talking Nan Needles, this is a personal matter nothing to do with the business. I admire her artist and she is a lovely young girl be side. Fatso says, thats right and she happens to belong to us exclusive. Wheeler gives, you are talking prof essional life. Fatso says, Im talking the whole thing. we are all legitimate and we like to keep it in this manner. Wheeler says, I like to assure you my interest in this girl is personal not professional. Fatso: youre interest better be nothing if not you got no idea the amount of unhealth is going to start passing around. so now we are telling you once so we dont want to have to tell you twice. we are just telling you what is what and that is that. Wheeler says, I like to prove some thing to you. if you step in here next door I introduce you my partner in fact my boss, and he will tell you if we are interested in the girl in a business way of any way shape form. come on. So we all go through a door and there is a different small office with secretaries and we keep going and he knocks on an other door and we all go in. Well. You may not believe in this and I would blame no body. Who is sitting behind the desk there. Well I tell you I am a party has had my share of rough moments but this could be the worst. It is only Jimmy Ace thats all. (Public Enemy Number One from the olden times) There wasnt a one of us didnt one time or a nother work for him in some way. And had some kind

58

of hash. We none of us layed an eye on the other since godknows. There he was the same shorty with the cocky puss and well dressed. Wheeler says, Jimmy these fellows got an idea that. Jimmy Ace gets up and he walks over and he gives his pants a little hitch up with his elbow parts like he always use to and he says, I know I know. Than he looks to us and he says, why dont you bums leave the kids alone. Than he walks over and gives each one a shake of the hands and says, goodbye.

8

Downstairs, we take a taxi. No body talks a long time. Legs says, mistake. we should of worked him over last week. Fatso says, when the time comes. Going up against Jimmy Ace that is a thing you have to turn over in your mind. Legs says, sooner or later we are going to have to go up against him so why not now. Fatso says, hows this. I get Jimmy on the phone and I tell him after all we are all from the way back so we understand one the other and he should get the boy out of our hair if not we are going to open up. not on Jimmy, on Wheeler. Legs says, that is a good strategy. Skin gets mad. He says, you guys are beg inning to give me a pain some place. you are so old fashion you dont know what time is it. this guy he is an executive. and big business. you start with him the next thing some body is going to get jugged. dont forget every body in this cab has got some bad reputations. also I am thinking of Jimmy Ace in the case he dont see it your way.

Fatso says, so what do you say do. sit still and let them pull our rug under us? Skin says, no. but like you told him. how would he like it we footsied his propertys. see what I mean. we should let him know by registered mail if he dont lay off we are going to move in on him and grab off one of his propertys. Fatso says, nothing in writing would be better. I say, Eddie Miller would be the one to grab off. he is going like a bad out of hell these days. Fatso says, you have may be got some thing. we will see.

We saw. What we saw was we could of saved up the money for the phone calls because him an Nan kept right up. Like a regular heart team. The way it come to a head was I was suppose to take her over for a color shot for the New York Daily News and when I get there the maid (she had a maid) the maid tells me she is gone. Gone where? She had a lunch in date to meet some body Twenty-One. I go over there. I look around. She is naturally with Wheeler. I step over. He stands up. (He was all the time standing up this jerk) I say to Nan, what about the color shot. She says, oh was that today. I say, well it wasnt next decor ation day. She says, Im sorry but I will be a little late. I look at them both and I say, it could be later then you think. (Pretty good) And I blow.

I go back and I spill. Fatso picks to get sore and blast ME. I am trying to ask him what did I do but it is no use he is fit to be tired. Number one he is for going over there and grabbing her out by the hairs. I say to him, listen Fatso, it is no good having this kid if she is going to stop having the mood to sing. But he is not listening to no

63

thing. And the plumbing is standing out in his neck like he is going to bust some thing for sure. So he calls up Legs and while he is doing it he tells me call up Skin to come right over.

Pretty soon we are in a real confab. This one the shades are down and all the doors locked and every body is talking soft. It was just like in the olden days. What we are figu ring out is how to handle this nab because that is what we figured out we should do. It was decided Eddie Miller. There is a lot of reasons for this. First of all, he was the nu mber one draw-ing card on every Machine. Also, he was a strictly Wheeler proposition. Next of all, he was a man and this is better if there is going to be any fancy work. An other thing he was playing the Roxy so he is easy to put your hands upon. Legs is the one who took the charge of. Because of him having been mixed up in several good "snatches" and had the experience of it. He told how the best one he ever done was with an ambulance where all dressed up in white suits and walk in and do the pickup like that and carry this person out on a stretcher and went right through the city blowing a siren. Fatso dont like this idea, so Legs says there is a nother one with a closed delivery truck where you can handle some body in the back with out any body looking. Fatso says why not just a plain auto. Legs says, go to it if you want but not with me because this is no candy job, this kind of a boy he has got a crowd out side and if he sees him self winding up in a strange automobile whats more with strange characters he is liable to out cry or some thing foolish like that than

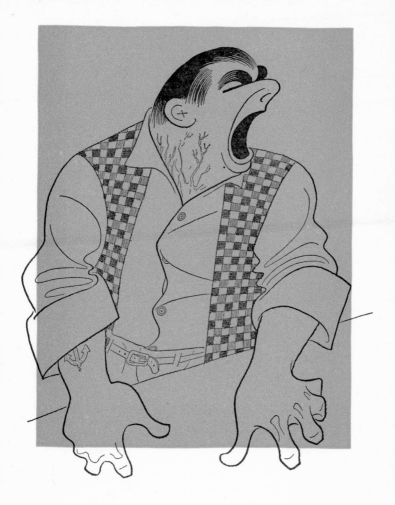

where are you. Fatso says, you handle it and tell us what.

So what we done was like this: Legs got this delivery truck (florist) and it is pulled up along side of across the street of the stage door of the Roxy. It is half past eleven thirty night. Skin is driving. Fatso is in the back of the truck with a little equipment. Legs and me are mingling with the crowd out in the front. We have both got our autograph books with us (not real) and we are trying to get close to the door. Pretty soon out comes Eddie Miller with a few friends and managers. So the way Legs showed me I get Eddie Miller loose from his friends and managers and keep shoving. Legs gets a good hold around on Miller and the mean time Skin pulls the car over and one two three Legs has got the back of Eddie Millers coat over the top of his head and no body knows who is any body or where and boff in to the truck and the pull off. Fatso drags him back in the back and that is all I know because I am left with the crowd on the street all mulling around trying to get the autograph. So pretty soon I go. When I look back there is still confusion around the place there. I get my self a double rye and than I take a hack up town to the studio where the recording is set up. We have got Sid Bloomer there with a good pick up band and he has decided the best thing for this kind of emergency is to use a standard like MELANCHOLY. Because he says a tune like this Eddie Miller is bound to know and it does not waste the time.

By the time I get there I figure they are going to be

good and started all ready but I am wrong. I look in and there is the band. They are all wearing them headbags Legs had made up for every body (Thelmas mother made them) In the corner is Fatso and Legs and Skin (with headbags) and Eddie Miller (sore). This reminds me so I put on my headbag from my pocket and I go on in.

Big beef is going on. This Eddie Miller turns out to be brave and dumb which comes from being young. He is saying he is not going to record no number and what is this any how. Legs is talking, you must think we are some bunch of rover boys here boy but your making your self a hot mistake because you are going to record two sides if we got to stay in til cows give beer. At this point he takes off his benny and when this Miller kid saw the two holsters and the two what was in them he got white and it was like he never saw any thing like that before and he says, lets go. But he says it in like a whisper. Bloomer hands him the lyric sheet and they try out the key. Miller listens and than makes with his hand: down. So they do it lower and the guys in the booth get set (also headbags) and the red light hits. We are all sitting there watching. I have to admit them two holsters on Legs making me even a little jumpy my self. They looked so dis-agreeable

The band plays the intro and sounds good only Eddie Miller is looking at us four sitting there and he tries to sing only nothing comes (of his mouth) only a little squeak now and than and so after a while they stop. They try again but he cant get nothing out the more he tries. So they bring coffee and that dont help and than a guy in the

band has got a bottle and even that dont loosen the kid up. He is scared and his pipes are froze and he is "sweating." Finely, we got Legs put his benny back and this helps but it is some thing like around four in the morning by the time he cuts a side and than they do the backup which is by the name of EVERY DAY IS SUNDAY. The end of it we put a headbag (no eye holes) on him and ours off and we go with him back in the truck down town. On the way Fatso tells Miller it is ok and no further trouble unless he or his outfit makes it so shut up and forget it and that is that. Miller says, just leave me alone and Ill leave you. Fatso says, that is ok. In Central park near to the Columbus circle we leave him out and that is the end of that night. What a night.

9

IT DOESN'T take long and this record is going great. They are asking from all over the country. The surprise is that nothing is heard neither from Wheeler neither from Jimmy Ace. Legs is for doing a second "snatch" but Skin says we should not press our luck. Now we set up a routine of some body always an eye on Nan in case of a tit for tat. Then it starts.

She wants to see us so we go. She is in her place in the Waldorf and she says to us, that is a terrible thing you done and I dont like it. Fatso says, you mean crewcut dont. She says, never mind him. I think it is not honest and I am a shamed. Legs says, just dont get out of line honey. Well there is a lot of back and forthing and it winds up her crying. She says, I am un happy and sick of the hole thing and I am going back to Tennessee. We say, you are going no place. She says, you know two can play that game as well as one can play that game. We dont know what is she gassing about but we soon find out. What happened was:

It was decided Nan make a duet record with Tony Barton. Fatso dug down deep and gets one of the Big

Boys to fix up a two song. It was great, named ONE AND ONE IS ONE. So this day in the session she does the number with Tony Barton. Enjoyable. Than Barton blows and she is suppose to cut a couple more sides. One is some thing going over big in the Waldorf. ITS ALWAYS MY FIRST KISS WITH YOU, NO MATTER HOW MANY WE DO — that one. Na turally the thing was to get a platter on it. Nan balks. We say, why. She says, I dont want to because it is silly. We say, how come you do it every night in the Waldorf. and how it goes over big. She says, I dont care it is silly and I dont want to cut it. Right here we should of been wise that some thing was funny but Fatso decides leave her alone for now.

That night I am in the Waldorf because it is my night to keep my eyes on her and Skin is with me to keep comp any. Wheeler comes on over and talks to us. Nicely. He says, you mind if I join you I am alone this evening. Skin says, help your self. When it gets time for her to show, I notice they got a new mike. I remember I notice it but thats all. She comes on and does the opener. We are tal king her over while she is singing. Wheeler is telling us how great she is and why. Than she is ready to go in to the second. She hits a couple cords and she waits. She waits and waits and we dont know what is she waiting for. She just keeps looking around like as if she is waiting for them all to quiet down. And once and a while she hits a cord. Finely, still. And she goes in on it. With the band which I never heard her do before, but I dont pay any attention because it sounds allright. And she does it. ITS

72

ALWAYS MY FIRST KISS WITH YOU, NO MATTER HOW MANY WE DO. She does it better this night then I ever heard and boy when she is through they are tearing the place a part. An other thing I should of noticed at the time, well I did notice but not enough. It was while she was singing this one, Wheeler kept on looking at his watch. That was all.

About one week after, Legs and me we are in a place up town trying to line up some new territory and talking to this owner of like an ice cream parlor where they got a drop in every booth which makes it worthwhile. We are talking to show him our point of view. No muscle, because by now we are well thought of what with the Eddie Miller MELANCHOLY, and Nan, and also one that is going great is I LOVE YOU BECAUSE YOU ARE YOU. No body mentions so long as it is going so good including Legs, so we never find out if he is wise that Sally Dee (the way it says on the label) is really him. But whosoever she is her record is riding so no body talks. Well we are sitting there talking with the owner when all of a sudden we hear coming out of his Machine Nan singing and no doubt you know what she is singing. ITS ALWAYS MY FIRST KISS WITH YOU, NO MATTER HOW MANY WE DO — that one. Legs and me look to one other and take off.

Fatso is not in the office. The girl says he went to Nan. We go. Skin is there too because it is his day to keep his eyes on her. Fatso and Skin are just sitting. She is not up yet. We start in to tell them what we heard up town and Fatso hollers, tell me some thing I dont know. So we knew he knew. Skin didnt know so we took him in the hall and we told him. By the time we come back in Nan was up and she is sitting in her bath robe having breakfast. A big eater, by the way. And they said along this line:

FATSO: You done a bad thing sugar and I think you ought to be a shame.

NAN: I am not.

FATSO: Some day you will find out who are youre friends.

NAN: I hope so all right.

FATSO: I am surprise you go ahead and do what ever that clown tells you. who got you where you are?

NAN: He is no clown that is one sure thing.

FATSO: I am older then you.

NAN: And he didnt tell me it was my own idea.

FATSO: It was youre idea to cross us up like that?

LEGS: Plain high way robbery.

NAN: I was only trying to make up to him what you did with Eddie Miller. only fair.

I say: We didnt have nothing to do with that.

NAN: I dont believe it.

I say: Are you calling me a liar.

NAN: Yes I am.

(I don't answer her. What can I say)

FATSO: I dont want you to never do a thing like this again.

NAN: If every body will cool down I have an idea I would like to say.

We all got coffee and she tells the idea. It is that we should get together with Wheeler in a combine. Naturally this means with Jimmy Ace too. You could imagine how hot this went over. Fatso called her, daffy. She said she was not and that she could not stand it no more all this fighting and arguments and so forths. And she made up her mind either no more fighting and arguments and so forths, if not she was going to dis-appear and never sing till for ever. Fatso says he will think it over. The whole thing over. We go. For once no body had one idea what to.

The next few weeks it was like a mad house. The reports are coming in and the one two three leaders are our Eddie Miller, Wheelers Nan, and the Sally Dee record. One two three either way they are going like a photo finish week after week.

One night Nan says we are all invited to a party. We all go. Some party. It turns out to be Wheelers flat in a pent house. No body is there only him and us. He says Nan has been talking to him about the combine and he has talked it over with Jimmy Ace and Jimmy Ace says it is ok with him. Because all over the country it is turning out that different slot characters are moving in to this racket and Jimmy Ace figures that with our bunch and theres we can give any body going a Mexican stand off. And naturally, Wheeler says, there is no use kidding you you fellows have got the two hottest things going with Nan here and Sally Dee. how come you dont make a few more with her by the way. Legs speaks up and he says, be cause she is dead and berry thats why not. Wheeler says, he is shocked he didn't hear about it. This is the minute Fatso picks to

laugh. If he didnt of laughed that minute may be the whole thing could of turned out different from the way I am going to tell in a minute it turned out. But when he laughed, Legs left. Mad.

The next huddle Legs tells he is sold out. Fatso says, who to. He says, I dont know. some lawyer. so goodbye and goodluck. any body thinks I am ready to be a patsy they can think some more. it is getting embarrassing and also he says, the way things are beginning to go, I dont think this is so legitimate no more and Thelma dont like it so I am quitting while I am winning. So he left. We talked it over and said may be it is just as well. Fatso says, Legs is getting a little old for the hustle. he will do better on his chicken farm. I say, listen with the bundle he goes back with I wouldnt be surprised he changes over to turkeys. Skin is looking out through the window and he says (sad) things are not the same as they use to. may be times are changed or else we. but there is a big differents in the whole racket game. Fatso didnt say nothing. I neither.

A few days after comes a telegram from Skin he is in Miami. He has powdered. He tells he is sold out and dont ask him why but that is that. (What happened was he made an other pitch to Nan and she cooled him off so he got mad and when he tried to give her this diamond watch (hot) she would not take it and there was a big tangle)

Nan cuts two more about now and both are the ones that really go over several tops. The first was that one,

HOLDING HANDS. And the other one I CANT GO TO SLEEP ALONE. (I was against this one on account of sounding dirty but the way she done it it was not) So we are going great and the cuts from the records and radio and every thing we are right in there.

10

THE next thing a jam. We notice we havent put a Mach
ine in two weeks in fact we are getting muscled out of spot
after spot. Fatso is desperate and tells me I got to round
up some strong boys from Boston or even Canada where
he knows some very nice hoods. This time it was like the
olden days again only this time I personally did not like it
my self. It looked like it was going to start to be noisy. My
nerves.

One night we lay for Wheeler coming out of his place
of business and on the side walk Fatso tells him if he is
looking for trouble there is a lot of it around. Wheeler
plays not guilty and we tell him about the muscle. Wheel
er claims he dont know a thing about it (turned out later
he was leveling, it wasnt him and Jimmy Ace was giving
us the muscle it was a new mob but this we did not know
at that time)

The boys from Boston come and the first night they
done a good days work. They went here and there and
bust it up about fifteen Wheeler Machines for fair.

We expect a come back but there is nothing. If it
wouldnt of been for me taking on The Information Booth

one night (Kay) we wouldnt of ever knew why. But it turns out she tells me, you know who it was bought out Legs and Skin? Wheeler. I walk out on her right in the middle of every thing and look up Fatso and I give him the know. He laughs like I never seen him laugh. He says, that is really some thing. we have got this clown by the shorthairs. we can bust him up but if he busts up he is busting up half of his own self. He keeps on laughing. The friends from Boston keep on hammering.

A few days later Fatso stops laughing because it turns out all over town our Machines are jammed. Not bust but jammed with some kind of slugs. The repair men cant keep up with it and we are going bats.

In the Variety there is a head line on the front it says: JUKE BOX WAR!! And it says about the smashing and the jamming and mentions names and says this new Deputy is going to put a stop by putting a man to trail every body they know is in the box business. (The way he thought of this he used to be a basketball player for the N.Y.U. so he thought of this) So from now on there is a guy tailing me and one Fatso and Wheeler and Jimmy Ace and every body. Lucky they didn't know the Bostons but for us it made it hard to keep in touch with the Bostons. It was murder.

On the top of this, goodbye, Nan. She checks out and it is any bodys guess where is she. I say to Fatso how about throwing out the sponge. He says, you chicken on me now, Ill kick your lung out. At that time I didnt feel like getting my lung kicked out so I didnt chicken. He says, we got to locate her. We have promised her for a big Benefit Tv and if she dont show it will look bad, or even worse. And if we tell she has goofed, it will be also.

We start in by getting a hold of her maid who claims she knows from nothing. Fatso puts down a c note and we keep on talking. The maid is looking at the c but she is still dummied up. He puts down an other c and the maid looks at the two and she is getting weaker by the minute.

Who wouldnt. She says, well I know she is not in New York City. Fatso puts down an other c and the maid says, she is in New Jersey some place. Where, he says. She says, I dont know. He puts down an other one. She says, Atla ntic City. An other one. She says, the Traymore. One more c note on the pile and the maid says, room eleven oh eight. and nine. Ok, Fatso says, beat it. She picks up the pile and beats it. I say to him, it is like buying tips by the yard.

Now all we got to is get to Atlantic City but we got these two glues on us. Fatso figures out this dodge where we dress us up with over alls and we go down and help carry out garbage in the back and take off in the truck. It was not too enjoyable.

The next we are on the way to Atlantic City. What I am doing with four rods on me I couldnt explain even now. Just one of those cock eye things you get in to when the going is nervous. Fatso is rodded up too but not four.

We dont talk much on the way. I am dozing along when he wakes me up. He says, if I ever run in to Wheeler again I am going to paste him and if Jimmy Ace I may plug him. I say, why all of a sudden. He says, it is bad enough to get out smarted but I dont like to get by some punk like that. I say, why out smarted. He says, because. we been smashing his Machines. so what. he is insured. but he jams ours so there is no take on them and no insu rance neither. I say, you are right. I never thought of it that way. He says, that is youre trouble you dont think. This gets me a little huffed. (And on top it waking me up to insult me) I say, well may be not but I thought enough

84

to think you right into this touch. He says, right now your in no spot to take no bows for this. I would of answered back and who knows what would have developed, except all of a sudden we hear a noise we seem to of heard before and we look up and there is that goddam gazoo band and they are in the train with us. How they tailed us when the coppers didnt dont ask me. So we start through the cars with them after us and it was some trouble to get rid.

Atlantic City we ate, than went in a place and sat to drink. Because he says no use going in in case of she is not there for sure. It could be she went like to eat or a movie. Also it is better if we get her by surprise.

Around one the morning we go over and take a double room in the Traymore. Than we wait a few, than down the stairs til the eleven floor. We go to eleven 08. And nine. He rings the button. We wait. Next thing a light under the door. Fatso changes voice and says, telegram. The door opens up and our clocks damn near stop than and there because who is standing there but WHEELER. And he is got on pajamas and like a half of a bathrobe. He looks at us and he starts in to close the door but by now we are in action and we fly in. To make sure of no trouble, Fatso unloads his rod. We are all standing there the three and in comes Nan from the other room. She looks like sleepy with mussy hair and a nightgown with a long you can see through it practically robe and it is no use but I cant tell you Fatsos face. He says, well this is great, he says to Nan, you piping off about right and wrong a mile a minute and it turns out you may be dont know the differents your self so great. She tries to talk but he dont let her. Than he moves over to Wheeler, still with his rod showing and he says, I guess you heard of the Man Act I hope. you are going to have a tough rap to beat boy. a Federal whats more. He turns to me (Fatso) and he says, call a cop. I didnt think I heard my ears right. I say, me? call a cop? He says, and make it fast. Nan says, never mind I will do it. She picks up the phone and Fatso says, get away from there and he goes for her and pushes her away. Where upon Wheeler dives and knocks him over teakettle. The rod goes off and I move in but this is where I stop rem embering because Wheeler comes up from no where and I get hurt.

When I come too, no Fatso. He is gone some place. I am on the sofa and the place looks to be crawling with cops. Nan is giving me a drink and pretty soon I find out. Wheeler is not going to no pen like Fatso said he is going for the Man Act. Not unless they got some state where it turns out it is against the law to with youre own wife. Because it turns out they are married, the two kids. To each other. They done it about several weeks ago with out tel ling no body.

But Fatso is gone and I am with four rods on me. Whe eler and Nan, I have to say they act good, but it is no go. No body listens to no body. The judge dont listen to them when they try theyre best for me. And he dont listen to me, the judge. So I get even and I dont listen to him. He is so stubborn he cant get it out of his nog how I

happened to have on me four rods. The lawyer tells him how two are props and one is not loaded and all that but he is a stubborn, this judge, and he hands me this six to ten. (Months)

This is how I wasnt around for the big Benefit Tv. But seen it on the set here in the sneezer. Nan together with Patti Lake and Diana Steal they done a great trio. While I am looking it, I think probably no doubt Legs is, also, on his chicken farm. Skin, in Miami, too. Fatso is looking I bet in Jersey. And me where I was. It was good just the same. In fact, better.

Well so that is about it more or less of how it happened here I am again for godsake. I see where I left a lot out but this is the rough idea. Like I said, I put this down on account the chaplin telling me. He said it would help me to see where I made my mistake. Come to find out I dont know. After all this work. Looking over the whole thing I dont see what I could of done different from I done. Like when I say I should not of thought of Fatso. Why not? He is the best. And the idea its self. I couldnt help to think of that. What am I suppose to. Not think? No ideas?

No doubt when I get out I will think up some thing else. I will half to. All I hope is it doesnt land me back again that is all I hope. Because that could make it four and I could get the Big Deal. May be I will be all right if I think of ideas but not think of Fatso. He is ok though. A right guy. One of the finest and most smart characters I ever in my whole life met. A lovely man besides and prince all the way. The best friend Ive ever had. And I hope I never see him again for ever as long as I live that is all I hope.

This is the ending of it.